IRISH LIFE AND CULTURE

WITHE
FROM STOCK

KU-187-963

IRISH LANDSCAPE

Gnéithe na hÉireann

le R. LLOYD PRAEGER

Arna chur amach do
Chomhar Cultúra Éireann

ag Cló Mercier,
4 Sráid an Droichid, Corcaigh.

Irish Landscape

by R. LLOYD PRAEGER

Published for
The Cultural Relations Committee
of Ireland
by the Mercier Press,
4 Bridge Street, Cork.

22364

SBN 85342 296 6
FIRST EDITION
1953
REPRINTED
1961, 1972

THE aim of this series is to give a broad, informed survey of Irish life and culture, past and present. Each writer is left free to deal with his subject in his own way, and the views expressed are not necessarily those of the Committee. The general editor of the series is Caoimhín Ó Danachair.

Robert Lloyd Praeger is best remembered as a botanist but his earliest researches were on the geology of the north east of Ireland and he took an active part in many archaeological excavations. In addition to his scientific papers he wrote guide-books, essays and an autobiographical work of outstanding interest. His long and active life as a field-worker gave him an unrivalled knowledge of the Irish countryside.

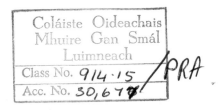

PRINTED IN THE REPUBLIC OF IRELAND BY
LEINSTER LEADER LIMITED, NAAS, CO. KILDARE

DUBLIN BAY

IRISH LANDSCAPE
AS SEEN BY A NATURALIST

BY R. LLOYD PRAEGER

WHAT DO WE mean by landscape? It is not too easy to
define. *Land* is inherent in the word, and *scape* suggests
a view or picture, the aspects of what the eye sees when
looking in any direction; and the word is redolent of
the open air. But if we know what we *mean* by landscape, we need not worry about definitions. The idea
of landscape is to our minds inevitably bound up with
the surface of our earth. Below the surface there is no
room for landscape, and above it impends "that in-
verted bowl we call the sky, whereunder crawling
cooped we live and die," concerning which we are
almost equally uninformed. But the flexible surface
with its amazing variety of aspect and its teeming life
provides us with an infinite field for study and for
wonderment; and for the satisfying of that God-sent
hunger that we call aesthetic pleasure.

For the purpose of this booklet, we accept a far
wider definition of the word than that suggested above.
Landscape need not be limited to what the eye alone
can appreciate. The impressions conveyed to the mind
are supplied in varied measures by all the human
senses, and form compound images often interlocked
and impossible to deal with separately. A scene may
be combined with a scent, or a sound may recall a
physical touch. So landscape as used here denotes
much more than what the eye alone suggests.

Ireland, with which we have to deal in the following

pages, is as regards landscape especially favoured among areas of moderate size on account of the wide variety of its physical and also its human interests. As to its actual frontiers, the turbulent ocean on the one side and the less formidable Irish Sea on the other provide around their margin an inexhaustible variety of no-man's-land where the waves have eaten into the rocks, forming dark cliffs or sandy bays; also the less conspicuous reverse condition where the sea has been forced back owing to a rising of the coast, resulting in new land planed smooth by the former action of the defeated ocean, and now carrying a population of land animals and land plants. Inside the shifting coast-line lies the main mass of our island. Though the surface of Ireland is on the whole smooth, it has passed during its history through great and long-continued periods of stress, when gigantic internal forces have here and there crumpled the surface into ridges and hollows, producing the delightful variety of form which we call scenery. Streams have deepened their courses, carving out valleys, sometimes wide and fertile, sometimes narrow and gorge-like. In a rainy country like Ireland, all hollows, large or small, are filled with water, so that Ireland is indeed a land of lakes. The central parts have for a long time suffered little from large earth-movements, so that much of the surface forms a great plain of limestone still retaining much of the horizontality which characterized the muds as which it was originally laid down under the ocean. At present raised some few hundreds of feet above the level of the sea, it forms a land surface much older than that of most countries of Europe. And a further point—the decayed rocks, mixed with the remains of thousands of years of grassy vegetation, have produced a soil singularly suitable for the food of grazing animals. So Ireland is and has been since man and his flocks first arrived, pre-eminently a cattle country. That is its destiny, and in the absence of extensive mineral deposits, so it will remain. That is its doom and pride. And though our carpet of luscious grass over limestone may not tend to produce for mankind the worldly wealth that would come from beds of coal or iron below the surface, who would not prefer the lovely verdant undisturbed countryside with its refreshing greenness, starry wild-flowers, limpid brooks, health-giving atmosphere and golden crops to the slag-heaps and spoil-banks, fac-tories and slums, which are the usual accompaniment of more wealth-producing conditions?

Ireland is essentially an agricultural country, with plenty of open space and little hurry or overcrowing; that is the main reason for its being so pleasant a refuge for those who seek rest after toil. The pity is that such conditions are, in the nature of things and the worship of "progress," ephemeral. We realise this by looking backward, not by looking forward. The urge for "im-provement" goes on incessantly. "The old order changeth, giving place to the new," even when the old was better in a hundred ways. I confess that, in order to envisage the Ireland of my best years, I throw my mind back for half a century. There were many "dis-advantages"—few bicycles, no motor-cars on the roads, no domestic electricity, no tarmac, no jazz (or worse), but there was less rush, time to think about things, and time to hold communion with nature, which is much the same as communion with God. But I believe that life on the present-day city model—incessant hurry, incessant noise and glare and excitement, and especially the deplorable craze for ugliness which is rapidly on the increase, carries within itself the germs of failure and disillusion; and that a return to simplicity and a less fervid existence will include a wider appreciation of nature and natural things. No doubt advancing years have a good deal to do with such a mental attitude.

'Tis "fancy buys the ribbon" an' all,
An' fancy sticks to the young;
But a man of his years can do wi' a pipe,
Can smoke an' hould his tongue
    D'ye mind,
Smoke an' hould his tongue.

So let us get back to the Irish landscape. Landscape in itself is in its physical aspect mainly the product of geological forces; and though one can admire sincerely a thing without any technical knowledge concerning it, one then sees only one side of the picture; some smattering of geology helps much to explain what we see; and in this human ant-heap on which we live the part which man's unceasing activity through several thousand years has played must not be overlooked. First as to the geological conditions which are the basis of all landscape, even in its widest sense. As has been said, the skin of the globe, which very slowly thickens when cooling proceeds, is still so thin that it is much affected by movement inside the crust. Apart from the sensational features of earthquakes and volcanoes, slow movement goes on all the time, and land and sea alter their boundaries; the various rocks which form the surface become upheaved or depressed; so that a map which shows the kinds of rock at present on the surface, upon the decay of which we ultimately depend for the soils on which to grow the plants which form the food of all living things, displays an amazing jigsaw puzzle of rocks of all kinds.

The Limestone Plain of Central Ireland, the most

A COUNTY ANTRIM HOMESTEAD

dominant physical feature of the country, is covered in the main with either grass or bog. Peat-bog is a very characteristic feature of Ireland and the Irish landscape, about one-seventeenth of the whole surface of the country being covered by this strange vegetable blanket. Out in the Central Plain the wide treeless purplish flat or convex surfaces of the bogs give a quite unusual aspect to the wider areas. This spreading peat is a very recent happening from the geological point of view. Our great bogs are only a few thousand years old, the operating conditions being the oncoming of a wet coldish climate subsequent to the Ice Age. In many areas the growth of peat has now lessened or ceased. The bacteria which cause the decay of vegetable matter lost their vigour under the wet cold conditions, and in consequence decay lessened, acidity increased, and accumulation of dead plants resulted, until up to forty or fifty feet of peat may remain, useless except for fuel (when dried). The surface layers of the bogs are generally so acid that a specialized dwarf vegetation has occupied the ground, of which the chief ingredient is the common ling, accompanied, on account of the scarcity of food, by some interesting insect-eating plants and others. At present the cutting of peat for the pro-duction of electric energy in particular is increasing greatly, and unless new sources of heating are dis-covered—as no doubt they will be—the problem of heat-supply in this rainy country will one day become acute.

The departure of that familiar Irish feature—the one-story white-washed house with its yellow thatch and its turf-stack (sometimes almost as big as the house itself) in close proximity—will remove one of the most characteristic Irish scenes.

Next as regards conditions affecting Irish landscape

must be placed the abundant rainfall. Owing to its position against the Atlantic seaboard with its mild moisture-laden westerly winds, Ireland is a wet country, and the frequent rain falls at all times of the year. The surface receives annually a precipitation of forty to sixty inches over most of its area, and much more in the wettest parts. Even the driest parts receive over thirty inches of rain per annum; even in summer growth is seldom interrupted by droughts, and there is in consequence justification for Ireland's name of the Emerald Isle. The presence of golf-courses verdant in August on light sandy soil excites astonishment in the minds of visitors from the United States or from the greater part of the European mainland. Rivers maintain an almost average outflow throughout the year, and the level of the innumerable lakes seldom allows of an extensive fringe of mud or sand. On the roads, even before the arrival of the invaluable tarmac, dust was rarer in summer than in most regions of macadam; but the roads of the past were famous for their mud.

Wind dominates Irish landscape everywhere. Even where actual exposure is slight, you have only to glance at the eastern inclination of the trees if you wish to obtain your compass-bearings; and the height of the tree-line, seldom great in Ireland, decreases as one goes westward till along the Atlantic coast it drops to sea-level; many Irish islands can scarcely boast even a shrub. In exposed areas the effect can be quite fantastic. Along the west coast in particular the trimming effected by the wind on young trees is accentuated by the presence of salt in the air, and dense dwarf growth results, in spite of warm winds.

The trees which decorate the Irish countryside are still mainly old native species—ash, oak, birch, alder, holly, willow, mountain-ash, hazel, black-thorn—much preferable and more comfortable to the general vegetation and aspects of the island than the close-ranked masses of foreign species that the professional forester, horrified at the relative sparsity of trees, pours into Ireland incessantly. Looked on as a crop—and an invaluable one—the "regimented rows of incongruous conifers" which are ousting the native vegetation are of the highest importance; but the day may come when we shall long for the open view, not for merely a tall hedge on either hand, with all the lovely prospect over mountain and valley gone—and as a palliative clouds of midges and horse-flies which are the real and only pests in this Ireland of ours.

The native trees and shrubs are mostly of only medium height and many of them are crammed with blossom in their appointed seasons — gorse, broom, black-thorn, hawthorn, rowan, and they regenerate naturally from seed—which the many imported kinds seldom do—so we may be sure that at least on poor soils and in wind-swept places they will continue to delight the eye, despite the advancing menace of Sitka spruce and all the other foreign invaders.

TOWNS AND VILLAGES

Let us be frank. Except in the vicinity of the larger towns, where a certain amount of metropolitan influence may prevail, or along the more sheltered shores, where influx of summer visitors connotes a more modern though not necessarily a more attractive standard of architecture or of hygiene, the Irish village does little to aid the natural amenities offered by the country-side. In the poorer areas it generally displays clear indications of the presence of an impoverished

11

and decreasing population. Too many of the villages suggest the phrase in which they have been despairingly described as consisting of a dozen inhabited houses, a dozen ruined houses, and half a dozen public houses. This is the effect of a rural economy betrayed by the potato, resulting in a reduction in population of one-half, accompanied and followed by many other handicaps. But that represents the Irish village at its worst. Conditions have improved and are improving. But most villages carry with them an indefinable Hibernian flavour, traceable in part to an Irish dislike of being *unnecessarily* tidy.

Some of the towns, despite the efforts of Cromwell and other improvers, are full of historical interest—Galway, Kilkenny, etc., for they have changed little since those days of mediaeval or more recent disturbances. The towns often have a quiet rural dignity about them unmixed with any excess of industrialism. Most of them retain their type of market towns, maintaining close connection with the surrounding country-side. The telephone and electric light make life easier, but the sky above is not reduced to a mere spider's web of wires—not that (except rarely) their place is taken by trees and flowering shrubs, as it often might be. As to the houses of the town-dwellers, they present everywhere an epitome of the last two centuries of unembellished domestic architecture. The only feature which is native is the long one-storeyed cottage, many of the older ones with walls built of mud, thatched roofs, and tiny windows which cannot be opened (the door provides ventilation). A periodical coat of whitewash keeps the walls dry and prevents decay, and the half-doors to some extent excludes the fowls and other intruders. In accordance with local rural economy, which favours small holdings, the fields are small and plentiful hedges

CLONMACNOISE

of thorn or gorse or walls of stone help to modify the wind.

BIRDS

The rather unsophisticated native birds that lend life to the Irish landscape are a great joy to those who appreciate wild life—and, one may add, who possess the ability to see them. It is an experience to spend a day in the country with a birdman. He sees a dozen different kinds to each one that you see, and every one of them full of beauty and interest and character. In Ireland with its open landscape and frequent absence of cover, there are plenty of birds to see. Rook villages full of noise and bustle in the early half of the year are, I fancy, commoner than human villages. What open view fails to show, if the trees are bare, the high-placed dark dome which signifies the last year's nest of a magpie? In hedge and field the birds are with us everywhere. But in Ireland it is to the sea-shores and lakes that one should go in early summer to see the birds in their glory. The sea-clifls are their citadel, and the sight of thousands of gulls, guillemots, razorbills, cormorants, puffins, tight packed on rocky ledges or grassy slopes, is one of the most remarkable our island affords. The lordly gannet is elusive, and favours the coast of Kerry; but most are wide-spread. The case of the attractive Fulmar is peculiar. Till lately breeding (in these islands) only on the remote Scottish island of St. Kilda, it suddenly began to spread, and is now a familiar feature in summer of almost every rocky coast. With its beautiful effortless gliding flight and snowy breast, it is a very welcome addition to the Irish landscape. In contrast to the native birds, the higher animals which belong to Ireland are usually not conspicuous. Of deer we have only one native, the red deer, which is a rare and shy inhabitant of Kerry. Then we come to the badger, hare, and otter, and after them smaller creatures like the squirrel and stoat and the rare marten; but all are shy, and do not affect the general lay-out of the animal kingdom as seen by the average man. But there is—or rather was—among them one—the musk-rat, which belongs to North America—which recently caused a commotion and but for vigorous action might have injuriously affected the placid Irish landscape. A pair of these animals in captivity at Nenagh escaped in 1927. They are burrowing beasts with a predilection for such places as the banks of rivers and canals and they are rapid breeders. The visitors made their home near the canal which conducts the waters of the Shannon to the electricity works at Ardnacrusha, from which much of Ireland is supplied with current. Here they increased and spread prodigiously. It took an Act of Parliament in 1933 and the death of the four hundred and eighty-seventh musk-rat, after a vigorous campaign, before the pest was exterminated, and Ireland was able to breathe freely again.

ON THE ROAD

On the lesser roads in country districts (often the most interesting) one notes a marked diminution in the number of the domestic animals—donkeys and heifers, goats, sheep and fowl—that used to share the thoroughfare with the human traveller. That is a secondary result of the arrival of the motor-car, and is a change that one cannot regret, although to the tolerant mind the animal friends added a certain interest to the journey. It is surely only a very unsympathetic motorist who will betray impatience at the donkey which can't make up his mind on which side he will allow a car to pass him, or the dog which lies stretched across a narrow lane, or the hen which is anxious to travel on the windscreen. But now-a-days such incidents are almost confined to unsophisticated lanes on which the surface is such that the rate of progress affords ample time to note the many charming things that nature has provided for our delight—flowers, birds and the ever-changing view. The wise man in such circumstances will cut speed to fifteen or twenty miles an hour, and will be richly rewarded, whether by some hoped-for discovery or the fact that that duck dodged just in time.

It is interesting to note that at no time has the distribution of important monuments of the past coincided with that of the areas most favoured by nature for the conditions of human life. It is true that it is in the more fertile and sheltered regions that we find most of the striking remains belonging to the Christian period—Glendalough, Clonmacnois, Rock of Cashel, etc., but the great pre-christian structures—the huge stone forts of Aran, Kerry, Donegal, the great megalithic cemeteries of New Grange, Carrowmore, the Dingle Peninsula, etc., show a fairly even geographical spread over the whole country in spite of the poor soils and wind-swept aspect of the west. I do not know how this peculiar feature is to be interpreted. To take the imposing dry-stone forts as an example: while the immense Grianan of Aileach near Derry is placed on a hill-top, commanding the country for miles around, the very similar Staigue Fort stands in a narrow mountain valley (leading nowhere) in southern Kerry— yet immense labour must have been expended equally on both structures. The Grianan blocks the entrance into the large and formerly populous peninsula of Inishowen. Staigue Fort has a position apparently of no significance at any period. In other cases of course the meaning of the choice of site may be obvious.

To go from the gigantic to the small. I never heard an explanation of the massive gate-pillars, built of stone and mortar, round, with conical shaped tops, and mostly white-washed, that one finds in many parts of Ireland—five or six feet high, quite imposing objects, and yet erected for quite trivial use—merely to hang a light iron gate on. They seem a waste of time and labour as compared with the simpler obstacle they often replace—an old cart wheel, or a furze bush, or the end of an old iron bedstead, or the ruins of a bicycle. But no doubt there is a philosophical explanation. (To keep the pigs in or out—you facetiously suggest.) Are they the descendants of some prehistoric type, or do they merely represent a way of getting rid of superfluous field-stones? Or are they degenerate forms of the Irish round tower motif, which they much resemble? But a tour in Ireland soon convinces you that the pig, far from being a universal animal there, is by no means so. The white-faced bullock is the Irish agricultural animal *par excellence*, and should figure on the Irish coat-of-arms, if any animal be so honoured; the harp, once favoured, is extinct as a national instrument, but exists still as an emblem, like the unicorn on the English arms. Another characteristic Irish sight, less common than it used to be, is the dense smoke-clouds caused by the burning of kelp along the coasts—especially those of the west coast—in summer. Formerly this industry employed a number of people, but now iodine is mostly obtained by other methods. The thick round stems of Laminaria, thrown ashore after gales, are collected, and dry by degrees on stone

THE VALE OF CLARA, CO. WICKLOW

walls built for the purpose. In summer they are burned into caked masses, giving out in the process volumes of heavy oily smoke. These white coiling wreaths are a very characteristic feature of Atlantic coastal scenery. The black caked residuum of the burning goes away for chemical treatment. The thinner parts of this and other kinds of sea-weeds are spread on the land as manure.

The birds of the wilder places have a special charm about them, partly no doubt due to association. It is not to the crowds of birds of certain of the cultivated areas—what we may call the mob-birds (rooks, jack-daws, starlings, as well as sea-gulls and other abundant species)—that we turn for interest, but rather to the rarer inhabitants of the less frequented parts of the country, where are found living less conspicuously what we may call the aristocracy of the bird world— ring ouzels and woodcock and snipe on the moors, dippers and grey wagtails and kingfishers by the streams, great crested grebes on the lakes, and a whole lot of others seldom seen, though they are often present, except by those who know how and where to look. These are for the observant visitor; but who cannot get rare joy for the presence of our common birds of the roadside — blackbirds and thrushes, bullfinches and chaffinches, robins and swallows, and the dainty tits. Then there are a number of higher animals familiar to observers on the other side of the Irish Sea, which he will *not* see in Ireland, but it is doubtful if he will miss them much—the mole, the voles, the common toad, and everything in the way of snakes and similar beasts. Zoologists say they were never here, while the country people prefer to believe that Saint Patrick drove them all out — believe whichever explanation suits your mental make-up!

THE PRESENT LANDSCAPE

The minor features of the face of Ireland have as regards detail changed and are changing so much in the last century that it is hard to generalize. Besides how can one generalize about a country which displays as much difference between Dublin and Inishbofin as there is between Reading and the Hebrides? The whole of Ireland is akin to Britain west of a line say from Portland Bill to York: and Ireland itself becomes less like England and more like Scotland all the way from the Irish Sea to Connemara.

There is a less obvious feature of the Irish landscape—a rather inconspicuous one which nevertheless impresses itself on the mind of the country rambler in his peregrinations, especially in the regions less altered by man—not conspicuous, but I think recognizable and important. This is the effect on the countryside of the folk-lore element; often taking the form of what unimaginative people would bluntly call superstition. In the country parts, and perhaps surprisingly more in the town than one might suppose, this influence is and has always been at work modifying the aspect of the landscape. It mostly takes the form of merely the carrying on of tradition; it leaves its traces all the time. Why is much of Ireland so infested with beautiful hawthorn, so that even good pasture may be seriously incommoded? It is because of a deep-seated prejudice against interfering with a hawthorn, for it is a fairy tree. Why is a magpie allowed by the farmer to build its bulky nest close beside a house, and to snatch the domestic chickens as they are hatched? Because it is unlucky to interfere with a magpie. A house may be built here, but not there—because the former site is on a fairy

18

path. This stone may be broken up and that one must not be. This widespread and mysterious folk-lore accounts I believe for quite a lot of the minor features of the country-side, which we might be inclined to attribute to mere chance. I have myself encountered many cases of it. And persisted in for centuries, it has sometimes made a definite impression on landscape, and accounts for what otherwise might seem meaningless. Much of it has for its abode the secret places of the human mind, and does not become vocal. In Ireland the vocal part, from legends down to present beliefs, is being driven underground in a mechanical and incredulous age, but the country is still full of it, as the world has always been if you have the wit and a sympathetic mental attitude to draw it forth. Here, for instance is a tale—true of course, so far as the shrewd narrator was concerned—told to my sister on the shores of a Wicklow lake, and given in the teller's own words—one of thousands of such tales found in Ireland, which, as I have said, still influence the doings of the country-side. The water-horse is an accepted animal of Irish zoology (*section* mythologia). It is apparently a near relation of the Lough Ness monster, believed in by many hard-headed people — even in Scotland; but for decorative effect it is inferior far to the Carrabuncle which belongs to the Kerry lakes, and which has "gold and jewels and precious stones hanging to it, and shells galore; the inside of the shells shines with gold." It is a matter of regret that it is seen only once in seven years, when it "lights up the whole lake." But if less attractive than the carrabuncle, its Lough Nahanagan relative seems at least to be more terrifying, which is also an asset of value. Here is a story of the Lough Nahanagan water-horse or *piast* as told to my sister:

"In ould days there was livin' in the County Down a poor woman that was a cripple. The power of her legs was gone from her intirely, an' she could har'ly put a foot under her. Well, there came to thim parts a wise man that was a doctor, and he gev out that he could cure all manner of disaises. So the woman sent for him an' asked could he cure her lame legs. 'There's no cure for you,' says he, 'but wan, and I go bail it's too hard for you.' 'Tell me what it is,' says she, 'whether or no.' 'Well,' says he, 'away in the County Wicklow there's a lake among the hills. It goes by the name of Loch Nahanagan. If you can get there, and wash your legs in the water of that lake, you'll be cured.

"At first the poor sowl thought this was intirely impossible. 'But still an' all,' says she, 'I'd be better dead than livin' this way; so with God's help I'll try it.' An' she set out. Sometimes in a horse-cart, and sometimes in an ass-cart, or maybe in a boat, wan way an' another she travelled south, an' after a long, long while she found herself among the wild mountains of the County Wicklow. An' the people there was good to her, an' two strong lads put her on a chair, an' they carried her up over the heather to Loch Nahanagan. An' they set the chair down in the lake a short piece off the bank, so she could wash her legs quite handy, and there they left her, well content to be at her journey's end.

"Now, at the bottom of this lake there was livin' a terrible monster called a water-horse. An' when the water-horse heard a splashin' an' dashin' goin' on overhead, he gets in a towerin' rage an' up he comes to see who darred make free with his

ERRIGAL

property. The poor woman was sittin' as aisy as you plaize, washin' her legs an' watching to see thim growin' straight an' strong, when she heard a noise, an' lookin' roun' her here she sees the fright-ful beast risin' out of the middle of the lake with his eyes rowlin' an' his tail lashin' out behin'. When he saw the woman he let a roar like a bull an' made wan rush at her. But, my dear! did she wait for him? In wan minute she was out of the chair, an' through the water, an' up the bank, an' over the mountain like a hare! An' she never stopped or stayed till she sat down by her own fireside in the county of Down. An' the legs of her were cured from that out."

The story is probably a well-known folk-tale adorned with local setting.

As a kind of frame for the whole Irish scene in whatever aspect—a kind of theatrical back-cloth—stands the Irish language—a vanishing though all-important portion of the country's general make-up, or else the symbol of re-conquest of the country by Irish ideals and an Irish civilization, whichever view you take of Ireland's destiny. The language is far from gone, and heroic efforts are being made for its general restoration. Time and the general trend of history will show. But at least we should recognize that, while the visitor will note the predominating influence of the English tongue in almost everything that is on the surface, the back-ground, the foundation of almost everything, is Irish. Take the place-names for instance. In the towns, cosmopolitan centres of comings and goings, we have our Grafton Street and our High Street and our Marrowbone Lane, but go to the country, even in the heart of old English or Norman colonies and you will find the Irish names are everywhere. This is of value to us, for these names are often highly descriptive, indicating physical features or personal names, or events long gone or still present, and in many cases making the past live again. Many of the words are now obsolete, and we are left wondering what they referred to. And as frequently they have got corrupted in the course of time, their identification may be a difficult matter. The Irish names are interesting, not only on account of their age and their appropriate meanings, but they are often euphonious besides; but others are difficult for an English tongue such as the *gh* in "lough" which is neither *lock* or *luff,* but pronounced like a softened German *ch.*

IRELAND FROM NORTH TO SOUTH

So far we have dealt with Irish landscape in a general way, including something of most of the varied factors which have gone to produce and to control it, whether of natural or of artificial origin. We now attempt a more close-up view, and to do this the best way will be to select a number of smaller areas chosen for their interest of one kind or another, but together conveying a series of vignettes which when combined will give a more detailed view of Ireland and what it contains of interest or beauty. We make our selection in a quite arbitrary fashion, preserving only a general sequence from north to south. In order to follow the rambling itinerary it will be well to have a map of Ireland at hand.

Donegal might be likened, from the point of view of landscape to a modified Scotland. This is due mainly to the fact that its geological history has been largely similar. The same ancient periods of deep-seated compression have squeezed the rocks into wedges and valleys, running north-east and south-west. But whereas the mountain-folds of Scotland still stand up starkly, displaying the very ancient rocks on which they were impressed, in Ireland subsequent movements and submergence of the surface have allowed later deposits, mostly of limestone, to bury the old folded surface and leave on top broad beds of limestone, old enough in all conscience, but still much less so than those they now bury. But Donegal now exhibits little sign of these more recent episodes, and mostly shows the ancient folded and upthrusted surface which we associate especially with the Highlands of Scotland. Though Donegal appears, from a glance at a map to be broadly joined to the rest of Ireland, the traveller entering it soon realizes that this is not so. The deep indentations of Lough Foyle in the east and Donegal Bay in the west approach to within thirty miles of each other and along the isthmus thus left all traffic to the greater part of Donegal must pass: behind this isthmus rise, ridge behind ridge, the ancient mountain-folds, forbidding easy access to the ocean and isolating the further lovelier regions of Donegal. Only a couple of mountain roads in twisting gorge-like valleys, wind through to the sea at Ardara and Burton Port and Carndonagh. Curiously enough, although the strong foldings described dominate the whole of Donegal, the principal sea-inlets that penetrate the country — Lough Swilly and Mulroy Bay — cut across these folds, forming scenery of great loveliness, where clear Atlantic water penetrates broken country of heather and rock and little fields—a paradise for the artist. Then again, in Inishowen (the peninsula in the north-east lying between Lough Foyle and Lough Swilly), there is, though the country is wild and rocky, and even villages rare, a remarkable profusion of early Christian monuments, chiefly crosses, some of very early date, showing in this land of bog and rock a former density of population which is difficult to account for, taking into consideration the rarity of such over many areas of fertile land elsewhere. The former importance of this area is also shown by the presence, on a commanding site, of the huge dry-stone fort known as the Grianan of Aileach. *Grianan* in Irish means sunny place, *Aileach* a stone house—the significance of the name is not now understood. It was clearly a fort, for the outer face of the wall is seventeen feet high and the inner face stepped into several levels; and outside the whole are the ruins of three concentric rings of earth and stone. It is a most impressive monument, and from its walls a very lovely prospect of Lough Swilly, the Donegal mountains and the Foyle valley is obtained.

The Ice Age mercifully refrained from covering most of Donegal with a blanket of deep clays or gravels as in Down or Fermanagh, and so the land is full of gnarled hillocks which provide a suitable setting for the gorse and heather and thorn and stunted birch which are characteristic of the lovely lake-strewn region of the Rosses, out to the west, which is sentinelled by the startling white cone of Errigal (2,466 feet, the highest hill in the country). This region of furthest Donegal is one of the most unspoiled portions of Ireland, and so is one of the most delightful or most dreary parts of the country according to the mentality of the visitor. The presence of salmon is for some a notable saving grace, with its usual accompaniment of good (that is, expensive) hotels. But the impressions that the visitor with a heart attuned to his surroundings obtains is rather one of lovely roads twisting through

24

GENEALOGICAL OFFICE, DUBLIN CASTLE

rocks gay with flowers, innumerable little blue lakes full of rare water-plants, cosy little white-washed houses in the hollows, donkeys and children and geese, dogs and calves, and off the fretted coast fascinating islets full of wild flowers and sandy rock-fringed bays beyond which after dusk the great light on Tory Island flashes its warning.

South-west Donegal offers a change, for the high and broad promontory of Malinmore presents massive cliffs and rocks to the sea—facing northward Slievetooey, and facing southward lovely Slieve League. The latter is a remarkable hill, a knife-edge which on the one side presents a cliff of varigated rock dropping one thousand nine hundred feet sheer into the ocean, while on the other it falls equally steeply into a small ice-scooped lake—a place to wonder at. Then we enter the deep indentation of Donegal Bay where at length we leave the picturesque domain of the old slate rocks and enter the northern fringe of the Central Plain.

Returning eastward to the region of Derry and Lough Foyle, we encounter a quite different land of quite different appearances and quite different age and origin; we pass from the oldest part of Ireland to the newest. This is the basaltic plateau of Antrim-Derry, built up in comparatively recent times by flows of molten lava which welled up through cracks in the earth's surface and buried this part of Ireland under level sheets of black melted rock. This, now much worn away by rain and frost and wind, still covers the ground to a depth of several hundred feet. The plateau has cracked and subsided along a north-and-south line, so deeply that the River Bann has found that its easiest course from Lough Neagh to the northern sea is down the valley thus formed. This lava is a rock rich in mineral salts such as plants love, and so the Bann valley and its surroundings form a rich and fertile region. The great lava-flows buried a whole series of older rocks which elsewhere, where not protected from atmospheric destruction, have been washed away. They stick out along the cliffy outer edges of the lava plateau and add greatly to the scenic amenities of the district, for they include bright red sandstones, white chalk, and blue clays. With their peculiar characters and bright colours they form of the coast of Antrim quite a geological museum. In many places the clays have slipped forward under the pressure of the overlying chalk and basalt and brought down a chaos of the rocks above them, providing a strange wilderness of black and white and blue and red. This used to be a remote region difficult to approach on account of the high impending edge of the basalt, but since the last hundred years or so the well-known Antrim coast road, winding along the shore, has made one of the most lovely and interesting regions of Ireland open to all. On one hand the many-tinted broken scarp, a thousand feet or more in height, and the waters of the North Channel on the other, with the hills and islands of Scotland—Kintyre, Aran, Jura, Ailsa Craig and Galloway form a beautiful spectacle. The fertile Bann valley to the west lies between the two edges of the high scarp, full of verdant crops and studded with factories engaged chiefly in the linen industry (for Antrim is the Irish centre of this important business). But the factories continue to fulfil their function without the accompaniment of a pall of smoke, such as accompanies too dense industrialism in much of northern England; here everything is fresh and pleasing.

As we approach the southern end of the basaltic scarp the ground breaks away, and we see in front of us the waters of Belfast Lough and beyond it the pleasant fertile fields and hills of County Down.

Belfast itself can boast of more "landscape" than the majority of cities, with its fine basaltic scarp of the Cave Hill, crowned by a prehistoric fort, impending over its northern suburbs to a height of one thousand one hundred feet, and the "pleasant Lagan" meandering from the southward through wooded demesnes towards the city harbour. "Belfast near the town of Carrickfergus" was the way it was described a few centuries ago. And long after the Normans under De Courcy built the imposing castle which stands intact on the northern shore of Belfast Lough at Carrickfergus twelve miles below Belfast, the site of the future northern metropolis—or at least of its central parts— was mainly mud-banks, tenanted only by herons and gulls. The Norman castle was built on an upthrust of hard volcanic rock on the edge of the tide, a commanding site guarding Belfast Lough. The city on the other hand was founded on deep beds of blue mud, and the central part is really a city on stilts, for buildings of any weight are supported on long piles driven down into the harder beds thirty or forty feet below. But outside the level flat the ground soon rises, and red sand forms a reliable foundation, overlooked by the high basaltic hills. The city itself, essentially modern, is compact; ways of escape into the varied and often beautiful environs are numerous. To the north and east rise the dark volcanic hills, sloping back to Lough Neagh, largest (but not most attractive) of our lakes. No less than three pleasant marine inlets are close to Belfast—Larne Lough to the north-east, Strangford Lough to the south-east, and the deeper and more important one at whose head Belfast stands. All three offer many points of interest and beauty, and the whole environment presents a variety of scene found seldom so near a great centre of business and manufacture. Strangford is especially pleasing, with its myriad gravelly islets, in summer tenanted by thousands of breeding sea-birds. Much of County Down—the region south of Belfast—is rich agricultural land, not level, but occupied by innumerable hillocks of glacial clay set close together—drumlins, to give them their Irish name—providing infinite variety to the setting of the winding lanes that wander through them. Strangford Lough is itself merely a part of this drumlin country set at a lower level, so that the invading sea has provided an archipelago.

This curious drumlin type of country is not in Ireland confined to Down. It extends in a broad belt from Co. Sligo by Lough Erne to Co. Monaghan and forms the remarkable archipelago at the head of Clew Bay, in Down it has led to the surface being likened to a basket of eggs—no inapt comparison. The soils of Down being highly tilled, a charming patchwork quilt results. I think the patchwork was more charming half a century ago, for then flax was grown in greater quantity, and the variety in favour was the one with blossoms of a beautiful blue. A field of this with its flowers swinging in the wind on their slender stems, was a very lovely sight. But the flax-plant of now-a-days has white flowers, not half so fascinating. Then, in former times, certain weeds, by no means welcomed by the farmer, helped to decorate the tilled ground—corncockle and bluebottle for instance. These are seldom seen now owing to the greater care taken by the seed merchants as to the purity of the seed which they supply. But the unwelcome weeds still often make a brave display. In summer charlock, in Irish *praiseach,* paints whole fields bright yellow, and later the corn marigold or gilgowan of a more golden colour, adorns

28

THE MOURNE MOUNTAINS

particularly the fields from which the potato leaves and flowers are fading.

At the southern end of County Down there is a notable change of scene, where the Mourne Mountains rise in a compact group of peaks and cones formed of granite—the highest hills in Ulster. They are of comparatively recent origin, pushed up through the thick beds of slate which normally cover them, and are a good deal less worn down than the much older granites of Wicklow, and consequently show steeper slopes and sharper edges. They provide ideal walking, of which now-a-days the Youth Hostels Association takes full advantage.

Now the coast-line bends westward round the roots of the mountains and enters lovely Carlingford Lough. This inlet of the sea has, perhaps, been moulded by ice between opposing mountain walls. It is awkward for shipping, and only vessels of comparatively shallow draft can make their way up to Newry which lies at its head. It is a very lovely piece of water, with the southern abutment of the Mourne Mountains rising steeply on one side and the rugged Slieve Foy on the other. This was a favourite haunt of the Norsemen in days gone by (the name is Norse, *Cairlinn Fiord,* Ford of Cairlinn) and in Norman times the latter invaders erected the imposing castle which in ruins still dominates the small town which nestles round it.

County Armagh, which adjoins Down, is an attractive fertile area mostly undulating like Down, and is notable in that its principal town has from early days been the headquarters of the Christian church. It has now two cathedrals, Roman Catholic and Protestant, and also a number of noteworthy buildings associated with its religious pre-eminence, making it a centre of quiet dignity and of pleasing appearance. Not far away from

Armagh city rises Emania or Navan Fort a gigantic earthwork and a pre-Christian centre occupying for many centuries a notable place in Ulster legend and history.

Along its northern edge Co. Armagh fronts Lough Neagh, largest lake in the British Isles, shallow, and with low-lying shores. Thomas Moore's fisherman, who saw round towers shining under the water as he wandered along its banks, must have had a very lively imagination! But its origin is sufficiently romantic without the necessity of bringing in round towers, or the Irish legend of an unguarded fountain. Long before the human period, when vast masses of volcanic rock were poured forth over the north-east of Ireland, the extrusion of so much material was compensated to some extent by an extensive local sinking of the land, which involved the Lough Neagh area. A large lake resulted, into which rivers poured sediment in such quantity that the original surface is buried under some thousand feet of clay and mud, on top of which the lake-water lies, mostly a mere fifty feet in depth. Lough Neagh is thus a great lonely sheet of water—singularly lonely, for there is little human activity on its shores, no towns on its immediate margins, and practically no traffic by water. The birds and fishes have it all their own way, except that one of the latter, the pollen, a very rare fish in general, is sufficiently abundant to provide livelihood in the season for a number of riparian dwellers. There are other rare animals and plants to be found there too.

The large county of Tyrone fronts Lough Neagh along its western edge, a large diversified county with bog-covered hills rising to what one may call the usual Irish height (about two thousand feet), but no strikingly picturesque features, few lakes, some fine streams, few towns or important object of antiquity—little, in fact, to tempt the visitor to loiter, except the charm of quiet landscape and pure Irish air. Co. Monaghan, adjoining on the south, also need not detain us. Cavan is a more varied county with some upstanding mountains and attractive lakes, little peat-bog (which character it shares with its neighbours). Like Tyrone and Monaghan, it is quite out of the bustle of the tourist traffic, but the observant visitor will find much to interest him. Fermanagh is more varied and interesting. It lies entirely in the basin (composed mainly of limestone) of the River Erne, and the River Erne may indeed be said to compose Fermanagh, for it is a remarkable lake-like stream, half land, half water, meandering from end to end of the county in maze-like form, a paradise for birds and wild flowers, more easily and pleasantly explored by boat than by road; and nowhere in Ireland are boats more used. The lake has a brief constriction in the middle, where on a small island the historic county town of Enniskillen stands. The area is well tilled, the smaller islands richly wooded, and its ancient importance is shown by many early christian monuments mostly safely placed on water-surrounded sites. On the Lower Lake (as the half below Enniskillen is designated), the land rises abruptly in tall limestone cliffs which look down on the more open broader part of the lake. It is a lovely region, and in England would have its praises widely sung; but perhaps it is preferable to find it with quiet scattered hotels, no roaring speed-boats (the many reefs would deter speed-fiends in any case), very few railways—just the mazy lakes and tall limestone cliffs and undulating smiling lowlands.

Above the lake the Erne continues its mazy course; below, it soon plunges into a gorge to meet the Atlantic at Ballyshannon and the favourite seaside resort of Bundoran.

Bundoran is distinctly attractive, especially if one has the opportunity of exploring its hinterland. The long straggling street follows the curve of the shore, partly rocky, partly sandy, on which the Atlantic waves, checked in their vigour by the long projection of Donegal to the northward, break with modified violence, and indeed sometimes as mere ripples. Near-by are the extensive sands which fringe the mouth of the River Erne. Southward the shore is rocky. Inland, a few miles away, rise the grey limestone hills of the Ben Bulben range, with the cliff-walled entrance to Glenade opening invitingly straight opposite; and a little to the south the bold flat-topped precipice of Ben Bulben. To the north of these hills, Lough Melvin lies, a delightful lake famous for its fishing; and the whole hinterland is a charming mixture of mountain and lake, of hill and dale. From Lough Erne down to Sligo you have a constant succession of lakes em-bosomed in limestone hills, and this type of ground continues inland so far as your petrol will generally hold out. Your best centres are Bundoran and Ennis-killen and between them they command a district of unusual beauty and variety, and full of archaeological interest besides.

At Sligo you are at the northern base of the great mountain-buttress of Mayo-Galway, which projects massively westward into the Atlantic in a rough semi-circle over fifty miles across, to rejoin the general trend of the Irish coast at Galway. This projection is pro-duced by the presence of a great mass of hard very ancient rock, chiefly slates and granites, which during vast ages have withstood the onslaught of the Atlantic better than less resistant rocks to north and south of

32

UPPER LAKE, KILLARNEY

them, and still stand boldly out, often in rugged mountains, but sometimes worn down almost to sea-level. The district includes famous Connemara, and all the hills of Mayo.

Of the three great rock-buttresses that in turn check the onslaught of the Atlantic along the west coast of Ireland, we now reach the middle one, which occupies West Mayo and West Galway. This is a region in which bog-covered rock is everywhere, and brown mountains plentifully distributed. This mountain-region with which we have to deal is confined by a barrier of lakes—Conn, Mask, Carra, Corrib, with the Central Plain lime-stones extending thence eastward across Ireland, and the ancient schists and other metamorphic rocks rising often directly from their western shores. The whole promontory is mountainous with vast bogs on the lower grounds, and a tattered coast full of little bays and inlets. Galway at the south-eastern corner is the usual and most convenient point of entry to this un-spoiled region. Railways there were—to Achill and Clifden—but the conditions have proved too difficult (in view of decreasing population and the arrival of the motor-car) and now if you come by train you disembark at Westport or Galway, and thank heaven that there is a bus in which to continue your journey into the promised land beyond. But the wise man will start westward on his bicycle—much preferable to a motor with its undesirable speed and the limited view to be obtained from its cramped windows as small as those of a Connemara cottage.

The road from Galway to Clifden (not bad under the prevailing circumstances once the preliminary piece that leads to Oughterard is passed) runs through heather and grey rock westward, with side-roads branching occasionally to right or left to pleasant isolated hostelries tucked in sheltered nooks—see guide books. The Atlantic is down to your left, hidden behind some miles of bog amid a complicated tangle of promontories and islands, while on the right the Maam Turk Mountains, and then the beautiful Twelve Bens, rise close over the road to over two thousand feet—remarkable hills, of grey quartzite, mostly bare of vegetation, evidently created for the benefit of the climber; for the rock is so firm and hard that a ledge an inch wide for hand or foot is sufficient to permit of progress. To the north, where the deep pass of Kylemore cuts the Twelve Bens off from Benchoona, there is some woodland and the scenery becomes less austere. North of that again the fiord of Killary, already mentioned, protrudes its long gorge far into the hills.

There are some picturesque ocean-girt islands off the coast here—Clare Island with its high cliffs and huge bird-colonies, Inisturk, Inisbofin, well worth a visit, if one does not mind rough water and primitive conditions. The large lakes—Conn, Carra, Mask, Corrib, which in a string cut off the region from the more hospitable limestone plain, are famous for their fishing, especially at may-fly time.

At the head of Galway Bay stands the old town of the same name, a place of historic interest and of strategic importance, for Lough Corrib almost touches the sea here, leaving a narrow neck through which all the traffic of the Connemara region must pass to gain the far-stretching Central Plain and the fertile regions to the eastward. So we perforce leave the mountain region of Mayo-Galway and keep eastward into the cattle country which extends right across Ireland to Dublin and the Irish Sea.

The name Central Plain is a good name *comparatively,* for in comparison with the rest of Ireland, north, south, east, or west, it is flat or flattish, but it must not be thought that its character is that of a true plain, like Holland or much of Hungary, or the great Russian plains. Central Ireland has endured, in the course of ages, much less crumpling than most of the Irish coastal regions, but its surface is in general undulating rather than flat, and the great squeezes that it has more than once endured have left plenty of relics of their presence, in ridges large or small, even in the middle of the flattish centre. Thus Slieve Bloom, conspicuous in the very middle of Ireland, rises in a long ridge of over one thousand seven hundred feet in height; the ridge follows the characteristic direction of Irish folding—north-east to south-west. But though hills are always in sight the general appearance of the area is plain-like. Grass and peat-bog, not crops, which are rather sparse, are the characteristic covering of the glacial clays which underlie them. Grass-land forms in some counties well over fifty per cent. of the total area, whereas crops never exceed one-third; peat-bog sometimes rises as high as one-fifth; a great deal of the grass land is marshy and full of such plants as meadow-sweet, purple loose-strife, orchids and rushes. Esker-ridges are frequent and often imposing, like winding railway embankments; they supply an abundance of limestone gravel, useful for many things. The majestic Shannon meanders right across the Central Plain from north to south, widening at intervals into lake-like expanses with islands of boulder-clay, rounded and grass-grown. Towns are few in this thinly-populated land, with few manufactures but a large market business. To north and south the plain gets more and more broken up by crumplings exposing the older (mostly Old Red Sandstone) rocks from below, and it ends vaguely, having touched the sea in the east in Dublin and Meath and in the west at Galway Bay and Clew Bay. With so much lovely country around the margin of Ireland, the Central Plain certainly cannot compete for a moment, but all over it are small areas of no mean order of beauty, and much of high archaeological interest—notably Clonmacnoise on the Shannon and the Rock of Cashel in Tipperary. The whole area is dotted with earthen forts, stone castles, and ancient burials, recalling Ireland's stormy history.

The Norse-Danish-Norman-English-Irish city of Dublin, centrally placed on the east coast of Ireland, has the advantage not shared by many European capitals—of being the natural metropolis of the country, as regards both internal and external communications, and the natural point of entry and departure. Here we are concerned only with its bearing on the subject of landscape; and in this respect again it can claim, in comparison with many capitals, a high place. The city, while possessing little that can be called ancient, has much of interest for the lover of cities, and is particularly favoured as regards its dignified streets and buildings of the Georgian period. Dublin's position as metropolis has resulted in the presence of a number of stately buildings and a certain dignity not shared by any other Irish town. Its situation at the head of Dublin Bay, which is sentinelled by the rocky headlands of Howth and Bray Head, is particularly pleasing, and the proximity of the mountains which rise a few miles beyond the southern suburbs and continue southward for sixty miles provides a tempting exit into the lovely hills and vales of the county of Wicklow. Inland there is less attraction, for the Central Plain advances to the sea, lapping round Dublin save on the south and ending in a low but picturesque coast-line.

South-eastern Ireland, like most other parts, is

CLIFFS OF MOHER

rimmed with mountains. South of the great ridge of the Leinster chain other hills take up the tale and, joined by more further inland, prolong the uplands till they finally merge with the highlands of Kerry. This south-eastern region is attractive — fertile soils, good shelter, and some fine rivers, of which the Nore, Barrow and Suir, coming from the Central Plain, unite to form the noble branched estuary of Waterford Haven. The coast here is different from anything we encounter elsewhere in Ireland—flat, and encumbered with great masses of sand and gravel, with lagoons lying behind lonely beaches. This results from the washing of material brought by the ice and deposited here. Reassorted by the waves, it now forms long submerged banks, very dangerous to shipping. Overlooking Dublin on the south rises the northern buttress of the Leinster chain, a mountain-mass which covers almost the whole of the county of Wicklow, and forms the largest continuous mass of high ground (over one thousand feet) to be found in Ireland. It is a compact area of granite flanked by slaty rocks, and continues for over sixty miles in a south-westerly direction. This upland represents a very ancient folding of the earth's crust, now greatly worn down but still rising in Lugnaquilla to over three thousand feet. Were it not for ice-action during the glacial period this mountain-mass would present a rather monotonous appearance of rounded heather-covered summits. But the ice has been busy here. Valleys have been sometimes deepened, sometimes choked with debris—both cases resulting here and there in small picturesque lakes. Steep slopes have been clawed out into cliffs with waterfilled hollows at their foot; bygone torrents have cut deep gashes across rocky barriers; and from our petty human standard, the whole surface has become diversified and picturesque; and finally the heather has spread, covering all the higher ground with purple blanket, mottled with green or grey with rushes or grass—a glorious playground for the people of Dublin.

Focus of the manifold attractions of Wicklow, lies the secluded vale of Glendalough, deeply excavated by the ice in the splintery slates flanking the central upthrust—two small lakes in a beautiful setting. St. Kevin certainly displayed rare discrimination when over thirteen centuries ago he chose this spot for his hermitage—though no doubt the choice was dictated by desire for seclusion rather than for romantic natural beauty. But Glendalough became a place of ecclesiastic importance, and a diocesan see. Its many small churches, built of stone, have survived, but of the civilian buildings—probably of wood—which must have accompanied them, no trace remains. The environment of Glendalough is delightful and the only danger which threatens its scenic beauty is the enthusiasm of the forestry people, who are substituting foreign trees for the natural vegetation.

The miles of beach which fringe the coast are a safe sanctuary for birds of many kinds, and for some rare plants. Inland, the country is pleasant and prosperous, with a fine river-gorge occupied by the River Blackwater coming from far to the westward. The remarkable flat-topped range of the Comeragh Mountains embosoms some of the finest examples of glacial erosion to be found in the country, Coomshingaun presenting a vertical cliff of a thousand feet high dropping into an inky black deep tarn—one of the finest coombs in these islands. The Knockmealdown Mountains, not far away, are a fine row of upstanding peaks of a couple of thousand feet high as seen from north or south, but this is chiefly window-dressing, as they form simply a straight ridge, without cliffs, lakes or other decorations. The Galtees, more to the north, are much more interesting, being considerably higher (three thousand and fifteen feet, a height rarely exceeded among Irish mountain-ranges), with steep slopes and some fine glacial coombs with tarns.

We come finally to the grand county of Kerry, which includes the most westerly portion of Ireland, and a good deal of its finest scenery. Like so much of Ireland, its striking topography is due to ancient intense folding of rocks of Carboniferous or Devonian age. The latter, exposed by denudation over wide areas, stand up in a series of noble ridges running into the Atlantic in a south-west direction, with the Carboniferous, now largely worn away, appearing in the valley-bottoms. The Devonian rocks consist of red and purple slates, and are hard and rugged, and project as long rocky ridges into the ocean, diminishing in height till at length they meet the ocean in a series of bold head-lands and picturesque islets. The ocean inlets inserted between them are deep, and give rise to much very lovely scenery. Inland, where the limestone still remains, is the famous lower lake of Killarney, formed by solution at the foot of lofty hills of sandstone and slate. The main cause of the exceptional beauty of the place is due to the solution of the limestone, resulting in winding shores and fantastic wooded islets and promontories set at the steep foot of the purple-tinted slaty wooded mountains. The town of Killarney, with most of the hotels, is providentially set a little distance away from the lakes, from which it is cut off by the wooded demesne of the Earl of Kenmare—a blessing in disguise, for it tends to disperse the summer crowds of visitors over a larger area. But Killarney may be described as *half* a beauty spot. The northern part of its periphery offers but little attraction; it is the southern half, where the lakes lie up against the hills, which contains most of the combination of lake and mountain that makes Killarney so wide-famed a beauty spot. The Lower Lake is open, dotted with wooded islands. The Upper is long and narrow, running into the hills among exquisite wooded slopes. The woods contain an abundance of the rare Mediterranean tree, Arbutus, which is native here, and a wealth of rare plants, among which a remarkable display of filmy-ferns, mosses and hepatics make the place a mecca for botanists far beyond the confines of Europe.

Killarney is the most sensational as it is the most populous place that the county Kerry can offer; but many people will prefer the far-stretching combination of ocean and hill that the great inlets offer. Glengarriff (across the Cork border), Kenmare, Parknasilla, Waterville, Valencia, and the grand Dingle Peninsula all spell exquisite scenery and country of high interest—the last two somewhat out of the tourist area, and in many ways no worse for that. The finest hill in all Kerry is Brandon, rising on the edge of the ocean on the Dingle Peninsula, lonely and spectacular, with gigantic cliffs and deep coombs—a marvellous place for the nature-lover who does not rejoice in the prospect of a luxury hotel waiting open-mouthed for him at the bottom of the hill! But he will find reasonable comfort all the same.

Of other places mentioned, I confess to a love for Kenmare, at the head of the long inlet of the Atlantic called the Kenmare River. There is a choice of hotels, larger or smaller; there are five roads radiating in as many directions through the mountains; there is Killarney only a few miles away; there is an infinite variety of hill and dale and lake, and unspoiled open ground. Parknasilla is a high favourite; Glengarriff, just over the Cork border, is a place of amazing attraction, situated on a marine bay full of islands, and the mildest place in the whole of Ireland, frost being practically unknown. Caragh Lake is beautifully situated; and there is Waterville and Dingle. If you want a really exciting adventure, attempt an expedition to the Skelligs, eight miles out in the open Atlantic off Valencia. Two islets, lying in the full sweep of the Atlantic billows, rise out of deep water like cathedrals, the larger to a height of seven hundred and fourteen feet; the smaller houses in summer a vast breeding crowd of gannets, the other, still more surprisingly, the ruins of a colony, long since abandoned, left by human beings, hermits in this impossible spot for a life of meditation and prayer. Their houses and churches, erected on the precipitous slopes, have bee-hive huts as domiciles and oratories and chapels, all of dry-built masonry. Eight miles out in the Atlantic, and landing often impossible even in summer. What a life! Now the storm petrels lay their eggs in the crevices of the anchorites primitive masonry.

SAOL AGUS CULTÚR IN ÉIRINN

The following booklets have been published
in this series:

I. THEATRE IN IRELAND by Micheál Mac
Liammóir.
II. POETRY IN MODERN IRELAND by Austin Clarke.
III. IRISH FOLK MUSIC, SONG AND DANCE by
Donal O'Sullivan.
IV. IRISH LANDSCAPE by R. Lloyd Praeger.
V. CONAMARA by Seán Mac Giollarnáth.
VI. IRISH CLASSICAL POETRY by Eleanor Knott.
VII. THE PERSONALITY OF LEINSTER by Maurice
Craig.
VIII. EARLY IRISH SOCIETY. Edited by Myles Dillon.
IX. THE FORTUNES OF THE IRISH LANGUAGE by
Daniel Corkery.
(No longer available in this series)
X. SAGA AND MYTH IN ANCIENT IRELAND by
Gerard Murphy.
XI. THE OSSIANIC LORE AND ROMANTIC TALES OF
MEDIEVAL IRELAND by Gerard Murphy.
XII. SOCIAL LIFE IN IRELAND, 1800-45. Edited by
R. B. McDowell.
XIII. DUBLIN by Desmond F. Moore.
XIV. THE IRISH LANGUAGE by David Greene.
XV. IRISH FOLK CUSTOM AND BELIEF by Seán
Ó Súilleabháin.
XVI. THE IRISH HARP by Joan Rimmer.
XVII. ERIUGENA by John J. O'Meara.
XVIII. WRITING IN IRISH TODAY by David Greene.

SPECIAL SERIES:
EARLY CHRISTIAN IRISH ART by Françoise Henry
(available also in French under the title
Art Irlandais. The translation from the
French is by Máire MacDermott).
IRISH HIGH CROSSES by Françoise Henry
(available also in French under the title
Croix Sculptées Irlandaises).